Seek and Find

Pirate

Pirate Dan and the mystery map

Young Daniel has never been on a pirate ship before, but all that is about to change! He is made captain of his very own boat, with a crazy crew to help him in the hunt for hidden treasure. You can be sure there will be some thrills and spills along the journey!

Dan could use a helping hand to search for lots of hidden items along the way. That's where you come in! Your eagle eyes will be an enormous boost on this pirate adventure. There are lots of items to look for on every page.

Daniel has a special key chain that he carries wherever he goes. Collect the five different charms on every step of his journey across the oceans.

The charms are:

- a steering wheel
- a star
- an anchor
- a skull
- a bone

Keep your eye out for five gold coins to add to the pirate-chest in each new location too!

There are also lists of other special items to look out for on every page.

Daniel has a sidekick who isn't always helpful. This pesky parrot likes to hide things from the pirates, sometimes in the most unusual places.

Super seek and find

All the animals, plants and items here can be found somewhere in this book. The pesky parrot knows where they are, but do you? Simply search the pages to find them. Don't forget to look in unusual places!

10 Dogs
5 Baskets of laundry
7 Purple palm trees
6 Violins
9 Ghosts of Davy Jones
5 Telescopes
5 Cannons
8 Bats
4 Striped socks
4 Lighthouses
5 Buckets
5 Spades
7 Goats
7 Messages in bottles
11 Blue starfish
3 Yummy cupcakes

Finally, on the last page of the book you will find a list of all the things the parrot has stolen.

Can you find them all?

Down at the docks

Daniel is clambering over the rocks.

He likes to watch pirate ships down at the docks.

But wait – who's this character coming his way?

He tells Daniel to go on a voyage today.

He hands him a map and points to a boat.

"Join those pirates!" he says. "For a new life afloat!"

Can you help Daniel find these items?

12 Rats

1 Crow's nest

3 Pirate flags

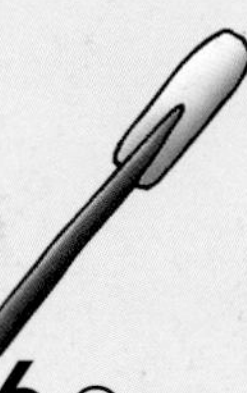

6 Oars

5 Bottles

4 Keys

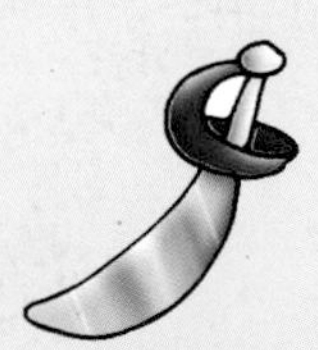

6 Cutlasses

7 Sacks of grain

23 Bunting flags

5 Barrels

Setting sail

The pirate ship needs a new captain, it seems.

So Daniel takes charge of all of the teams.

His parrot shouts orders: "First, swab the decks!"

He sits on Dan's shoulder where he squawks and he pecks.

He keeps stealing Dan's key chain and being a pest.

Look – there's a marble – can you find the rest?

Can you help Daniel find these items?

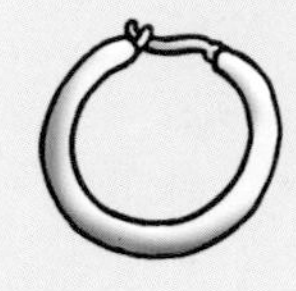

5 Gold hoop earrings

2 Packs of cards

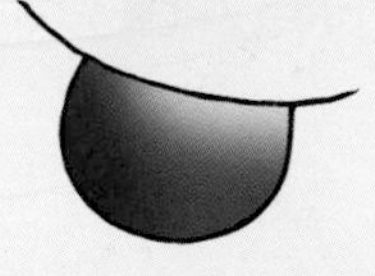

3 Eyepatches

8 Feathers

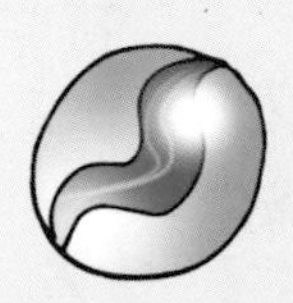

7 Marbles

8 Books

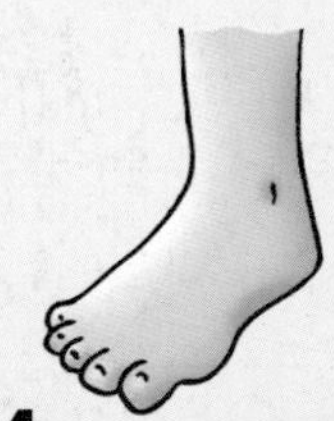

4 Bare feet

15 Cannon-balls

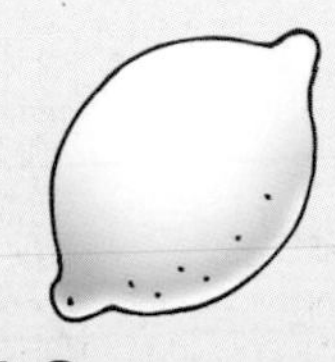

10 Lemons

7 Woodworms

Can you help Daniel find these items?
6 Sharks
5 Mermaid tails
12 Limpet shells
1 Silver anchor

All at sea

Daniel is loving his life on the ship,

And the pirates seem glad that he's there on the trip.

Together they see the most fabulous things,

Like mermaids and narwhals and fish that have wings.

They do battle with monsters that give them a fright,

But Daniel is brave, and they win every fight.

8 Flying fish

2 Peeping pirates

4 Socks with holes

15 Spiders

7 Clouds

Mouths to feed

They've been sailing for weeks and supplies are now low.
Dan's map shows an island, so that's where they'll go.
The cook does his best with the food that they've got,
But the pirates are hungry; there isn't a lot.
They have maggoty crumble and salad with bugs,
But Dan draws the line at the stew made from slugs.

Can you help Daniel find these items?

8 Maggoty biscuits

4 Roast chickens

6 Saucepans

7 Tankards

14 Mice

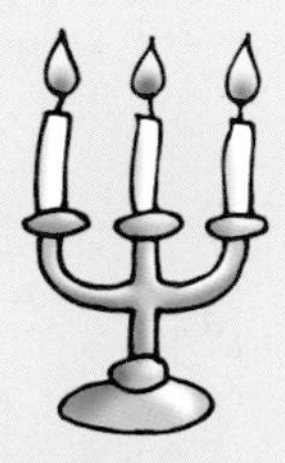

2 Candelabras

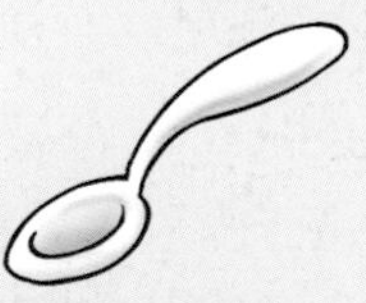

6 Spoons

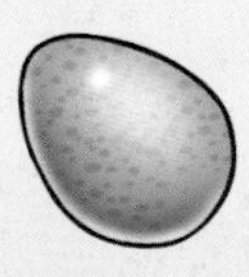

10 Eggs

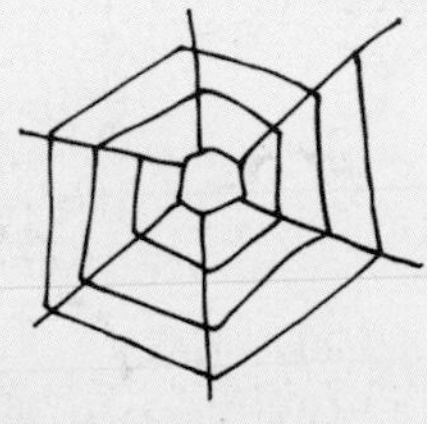

3 Spider webs

4 Potted plants

Land ahoy!

The pirates work hard with Dan as their chief,

But the parrot is naughty – a feathery thief.

He's stolen Dan's hat for his own secret hoard.

Dan warns, "Stop your tricks, or you'll go overboard!"

Then a shout from the crow's nest makes everyone cheer:

"Land ahoy! I see trees! The island is near!"

Can you help Daniel find these items?

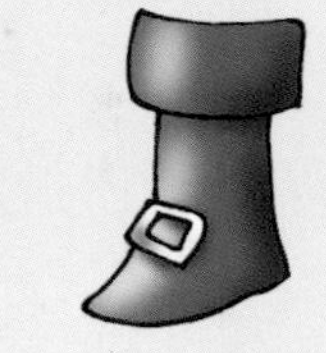

6 Pirate boots

11 Seagulls

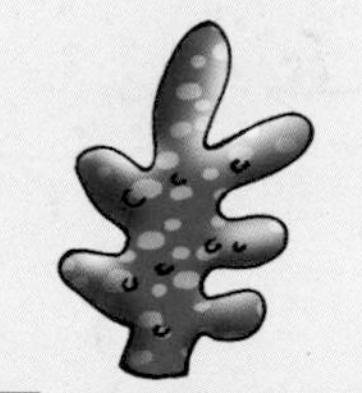

7 Pieces of seaweed

5 Turtles

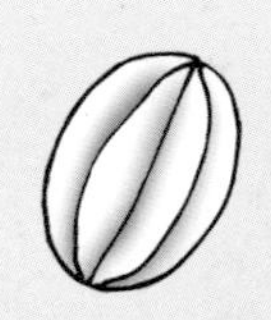

8 Starfruit

3 Smoking fires

12 Anemones

7 Coconuts

2 Purple birds

6 Snails

Trader Jack's

Dan gives the order to steer them to shore,
Where they buy new supplies at the grocery store.
It sells many things, from ribbons to boots,
There are chickens and cheeses and exotic fruits.
They load up the ship with goodies and treats,
And the yummy biscuits that everyone eats.

Can you help Daniel find these items?

6 Hens

5 Loaves

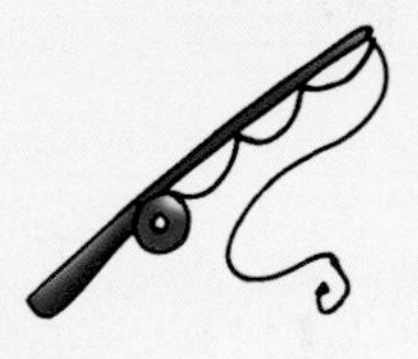

4 Fishing rods

9 Sticks of candy

15 Shells

10 Royal coins

1 Compass

5 Ribbons

7 Quill pens

3 Lobsters

Can you help Daniel find these items?
11 Pieces of wreckage
3 Puking pirates
12 Lightning bolts
1 Worried whale

A sudden storm

With lovely full tummies, they head back to sea,
Dreaming of what they will eat for their tea.
Then the sky becomes dark and thunder booms loud,
And lightning bolts flash from sinister clouds.
Massive great waves start to break up the boat.
The pirates are scared that it won't stay afloat!

8 Lifebelts

7 Inflatable armbands

1 Vase of flowers

9 Scared snails

1 Ship's steering wheel

Abandon ship!

"We're not going to make it! The ship's going down!"

They head for the lifeboats so no-one will drown.

Dan unfolds his map and they all take a look.

"We could head for that small piece of land," says the cook.

They work out directions, but progress is slow,

As they squabble and fight about who has to row.

Can you help Daniel find these items?

1 Scared squid

4 Lobsters

6 Eels

3 Penguins

4 Turtles

5 Combs

15 Pearl shells

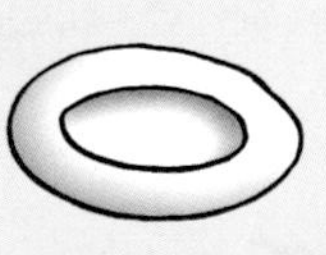

10 Dinner plates

7 Fish

3 Mermaids

Can you help Daniel find these items?
12 Pineapples
18 Bananas
4 Monkeys
3 Birds of paradise

To the rescue

Sunburned and tired, the pirates need help.
Their boat drifts around – but then Dan gives a yelp.
"Look! There's the island! Take us ashore!"
The waves wash them in, they can't row any more.
The pirates are scared about who they might find,
But the people who live here are helpful and kind.

A new boat

The pirates get used to their new life of leisure,
But marked on Dan's map are some caves that say TREASURE.
He plots and he plans and he chews on his lip,
Then speaks to the locals and borrows a ship.
The pirates set sail, who knows what they'll find,
As they leave their new friends in the village behind.

Can you help Daniel find these items?

14 Spooky eyes

4 Lanterns

7 Ducks

8 Nests

6 Portholes

7 Shells

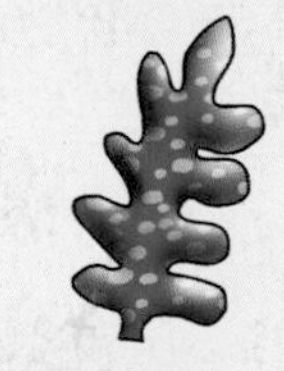
12 Ferns

1 Crocodile

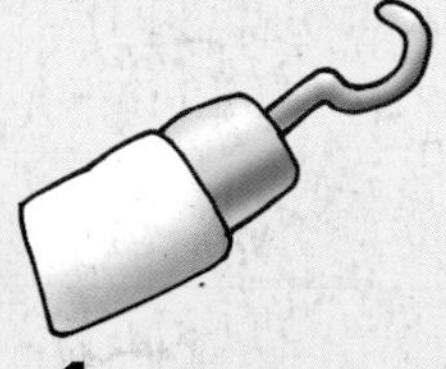
1 Hooked hand

6 Spiders

X marks the spot

They follow the map beyond the dark caves,
And find a lagoon with small lapping waves.
The map shows a white sandy beach, marked with X.
The pirates grab shovels and spades from the decks.
The sun blazes down on the men as they dig.
Daniel brings drinks and they stop for a swig.

Can you help Daniel find these items?

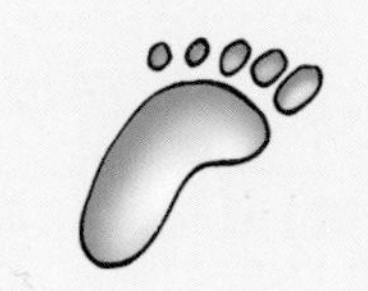

12 Footprints

5 Snakes

3 Turtles

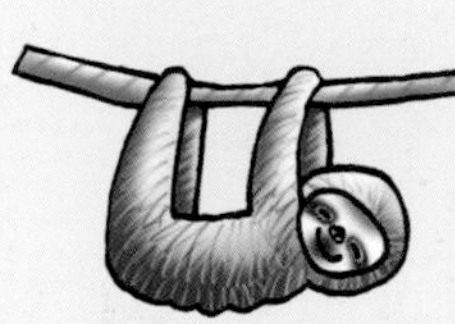

1 Sloth

12 Skulls

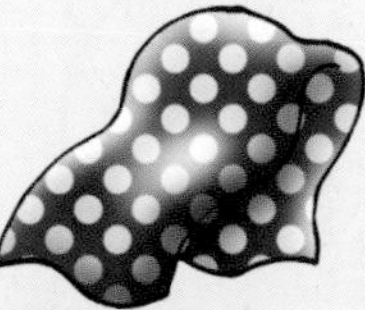

3 Spotted scarves

5 Cool drinks

13 Dragon-flies

8 Crabs

3 Ants

Party time!

The map was correct and they dig out a chest.

"Three cheers for Dan! We think he's the best!"

A party breaks out and the pirates all cheer,

They eat chicken and cookies and drink ginger beer.

The cook and his mate lift Dan in the air,

"You've earned your position as boss, fair and square!"

Can you help Daniel find these items?

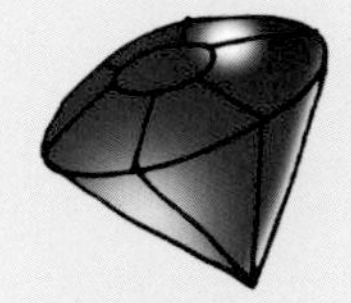

18 Rubies

5 Crowns

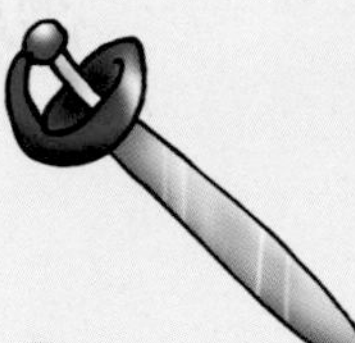

3 Swords

6 Goblets

17 Musical notes

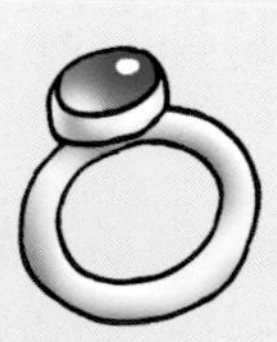

9 Rings

5 Patches

4 Belt buckles

10 Chicken drumsticks

7 Maracas

Super seek and find

All the animals, plants and items here can be found somewhere in this book. The pesky parrot knows where they are, but do you? Simply search the pages to find them. Don't forget to look in unusual places!

10 Dogs

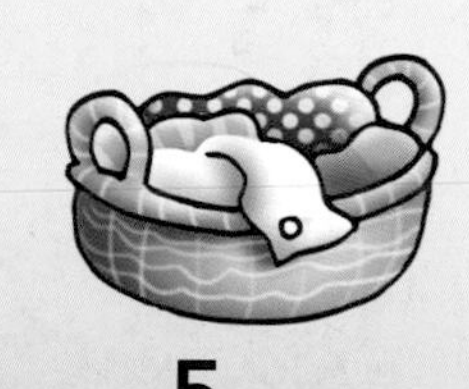

5 Baskets of laundry

7 Purple palm trees

6 Violins

9 Ghosts of Davy Jones

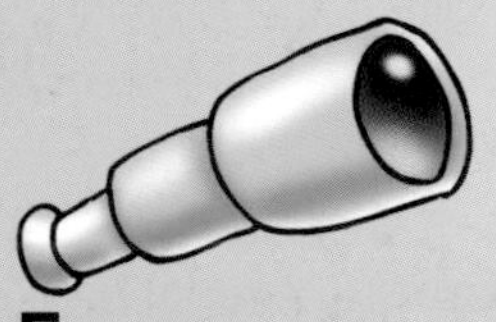

5 Telescopes

5 Cannons

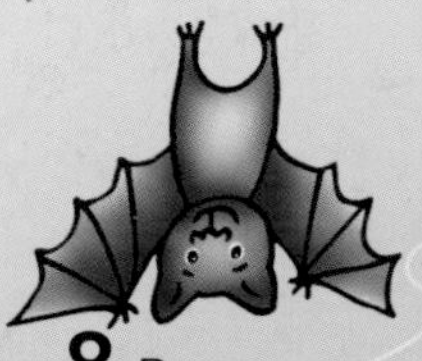

8 Bats

4 Striped socks

4 Lighthouses

5 Buckets

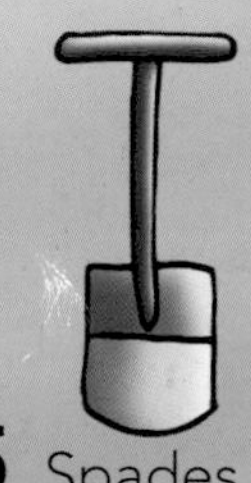

5 Spades

7 Goats

7 Messages in bottles

11 Blue starfish

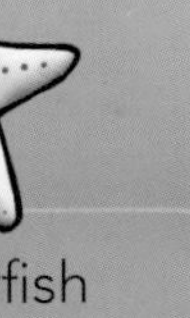

3 Yummy cupcakes